IMPORTANT SAFETY
INSTRUCTIONS

While the **Publisher** has used all reasonable endeavours to ensure that these activities are safe for children to undertake, there are some that require the **assistance of a grown-up**. These are marked with . . .

. . . in the stages of each activity concerned.

Young mischief and marvel makers, please make use of your grown-ups, and **don't try these alone**! Stick to the steps described in this book for **maximum safety** and the **best results**.

ROALD DAHL was a

spy, ace fighter pilot, chocolate historian and medical inventor. He was also the author of *Charlie and the Chocolate Factory, Matilda, The BFG* and many more brilliant stories. He remains **THE WORLD'S NUMBER ONE STORYTELLER.**

QUENTIN BLAKE

has illustrated more than three hundred books and was Roald Dahl's favourite illustrator. In 1980 he won the prestigious Kate Greenaway Medal. In 1999 he became the first ever Children's Laureate and in 2013 he was knighted for services to illustration.

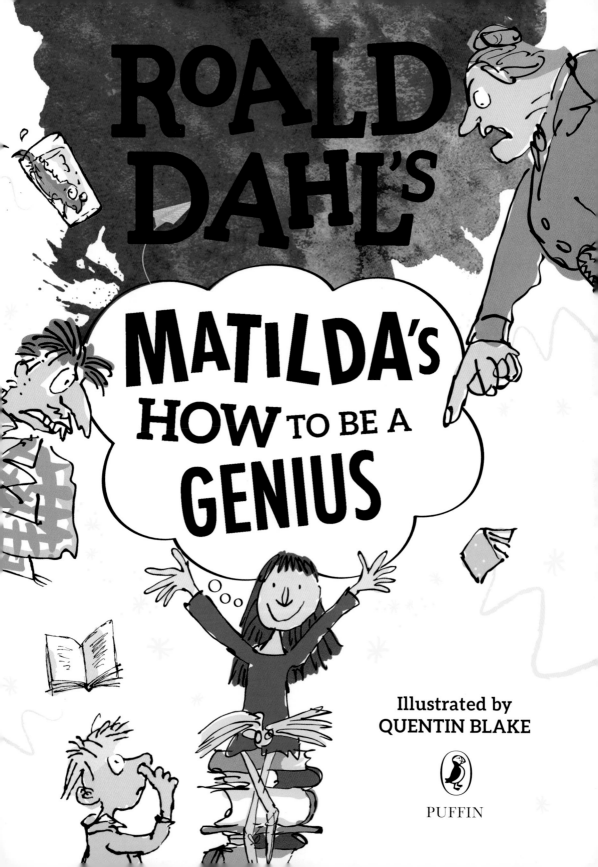

ROALD DAHL'S

MATILDA's
HOW TO BE A
GENIUS

Illustrated by
QUENTIN BLAKE

PUFFIN

PUFFIN BOOKS

UK | USA | Canada | Ireland | Australia
India | New Zealand | South Africa

Puffin Books is part of the Penguin Random House group of companies
whose addresses can be found at global.penguinrandomhouse.com.

www.penguin.co.uk   www.puffin.co.uk   www.ladybird.co.uk

 Penguin
Random House
UK

First published 2019

001

Copyright © The Roald Dahl Story Company Ltd/Quentin Blake, 2019
Written by Lauren Holowaty
Diagrams by Jim Peacock
Designed by Mandy Norman

ROALD DAHL is a registered trademark of The Roald Dahl Story Company Ltd
www.roalddahl.com

The moral right of the author and illustrator has been asserted

Printed in China

A CIP catalogue record for this book is available from the British Library

ISBN: 978-0-241-37118-3

All correspondence to:
Puffin Books
Penguin Random House Children's
80 Strand, London WC2R 0RL

CONTENTS

MATILDA WORMWOOD

An EXTRA-ORDINARY child
GENIUS looking for **REVENGE**.

'It is bad enough when parents treat ordinary children as though they were SCABS and BUNIONS, but it becomes somehow a lot worse when the child in question is **EXTRA-ORDINARY** . . . SENSITIVE and BRILLIANT. Matilda was both of these things, but above all she was **BRILLIANT** . . . She resented being told constantly that she was ignorant and stupid when she knew she wasn't. The anger inside her went on BOILING and BOILING, and as she lay in bed that night she made a decision. She decided that every time her father or her mother was beastly to her, she would get her own back in some way or another.'

MR AND MRS WORMWOOD

Matilda's really **STUPID** and
DESPICABLE PARENTS who show
absolutely no interest in her at all.

'A scab is something you have to put up with until the time comes when you can pick it off and **FLICK** it away. Mr and Mrs Wormwood looked forward enormously to the time when they could pick their little daughter off and flick her away, preferably into the NEXT COUNTY or even further than that.'

MISS HONEY

Matilda's KIND TEACHER who wants to help her and make others realize how **BRILLIANT** she is.

'Miss Jennifer Honey was a MILD and QUIET person who never raised her voice and was seldom seen to smile, but there is no doubt she possessed that rare gift for being **ADORED** by every small child under her care.'

MISS TRUNCHBULL

Matilda's **HULKING** and **HORRIFYING** HEADMISTRESS, who thinks all her pupils are rotten little stinkers.

'She was a GIGANTIC HOLY **TERROR**, a FIERCE TYRANNICAL MONSTER who frightened the life out of the pupils and teachers alike. There was an aura of MENACE about her even at a distance, and when she came up close you could almost feel the DANGEROUS heat radiating from her as from a red-hot rod of metal.'

BRUCE BOGTROTTER

The boy who DARES to STEAL a slice of the Trunchbull's chocolate cake and lie about it, and is then forced to eat an **ENORMOUS CAKE** as punishment.

'THE TRUNCHBULL was not a person who would give someone a whole chocolate cake to eat just out of kindness. Many were guessing that it had been filled with **PEPPER** or **CASTOR-OIL** or some other foul-tasting substance that would make the boy violently sick. It might even be ARSENIC and he would be **DEAD IN TEN SECONDS FLAT**.'

INTRODUCTION

Matilda's ENORMOUS BRAIN **fizzes** and **bubbles** with curiosity, but her rotten parents and headmistress think she's a liar and a cheat. This book is a celebration of Matilda's **marvellous mind** and how she uses it to rise above the beastly grown-ups and seek MISCHIEVOUS REVENGE!

In this book you'll find AMAZING TRICKS, mental marvels and short cuts, **puzzles** and **games** to TRAIN YOUR BRAIN, and even a sprinkling of magic! You'll also find out more about Matilda and other brilliant characters such as MISS HONEY, BRUCE BOGTROTTER and, of course, the **TERRIFYING TRUNCHBULL**!

STUN YOUR FAMILY AND FRIENDS with your powers of **mind-reading** by guessing their age, shoe size, and even how much money is in their pocket! Learn how to add **MASSIVE NUMBERS** together without using a calculator, and how to write FIENDISH RIDDLES to confound your friends! Write secret messages using invisible ink, poke skewers through balloons without popping them, and make exploding chocolate cakes!

These GENIUS TRICKS are all easy to master by using EVERYDAY OBJECTS, following **simple step-by-step instructions**.

Inspired by **ROALD DAHL'S** extraordinary tale, this book is for EXTRAORDINARY CHILDREN everywhere!

CHAPTER ONE
MAGICAL
MIND
Maths

MAGICAL MIND *Maths*

Matilda's **mathematical brilliance** is wasted on her ignorant parents, but when she starts school, her teacher, Miss Honey, soon realizes how extraordinary her maths skills are …

MISS HONEY had never come across a five-year-old before, or indeed a ten-year-old, who could multiply with such facility …

'For instance,' Miss Honey said, 'if I asked you to **MULTIPLY FOURTEEN BY NINETEEN** … No, that's too difficult …'

'It's **TWO HUNDRED AND SIXTY-SIX**,' Matilda said softly …

'Now tell me, Matilda,' Miss Honey said … 'try to tell me exactly what goes on **INSIDE YOUR HEAD** when you get a multiplication like that to do …'

'I'm afraid I don't know how to explain it. I've always said to myself that if a little **POCKET CALCULATOR** can do it why shouldn't I?'

'Why not indeed?' Miss Honey said. 'The **HUMAN BRAIN** is an AMAZING THING.'

This chapter will help you **train your brain** to perform bewildering feats of logic and calculation, and **clever mathematical tricks** that will make everyone think you are either super-brainy or actually a mind-reader! They include:

$$222 \div 6 \text{ or } 777 \div 21$$

Making the impossible seem possible with **arithmetic games**!

A genius game you're **sure to win**!

Guessing what's in someone's **pockets**!

ROWS	COLUMNS			
	3	0	0	8
	1	3	5	7
	8	6	4	2
	9	2	6	5
+	0	7	3	4
2	3	0	0	6

Working out **long-numbered addition** instantly!

$9 \times 20 = 180$
$180 + 3 = 183$
$183 \times 5 = 915$
$915 + 3 = 918$
$3 \times 5 = 15$
$918 - 15 = 903$

And even how to tell **someone's age and shoe size** using ... maths!

Astonishing
ARITHME-**TRICKS!**

MAGNIFICENT **MULTIPLYING!**

Matilda astounds her teacher, Miss Honey, with her absolutely **amazing mathematical abilities**. Practise playing these cunningly clever **arithmetic games** with your friends, family and teachers, so you can do the same!

1 Read these steps first, then ask a friend to think of a **three-digit number**.

2 Ask them to **multiply it with x7x11x13** on a calculator.

3 **You instantly know** what the answer is because it will always be the **original number repeated twice**. For example, if your friend chose the number 123, you know the answer will be 123123!

4 Watch as your friend finishes the calculation on the calculator and is **amazed by your brilliance**!

123123

DIFFICULTY RATING:

THE 3-DIGIT
DIVISION TRICK!

1 Read through these steps, then ask your friend to think of a **three-digit number** where **each of the digits is the same**. For example:

222, 777, etc.

2 Ask them to **add up all the digits of that number** in their head. For example:

2+2+2=6 or 7+7+7=21.

3 Ask your friend to use a calculator to divide their **original three-digit number by the sum of the digits**. For example:

222 ÷ 6 or 777 ÷ 21

4 Impress your friend by instantly telling them **the answer is 37** before they finish doing the sum on the calculator!

The answer will always be **37**.

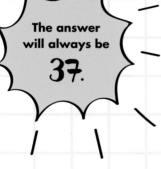

CUNNING Coin TRICK

Baffle your **parents and classmates** by channelling Matilda's mathematical genius to guess **how much money** they have in their pockets!

DIFFICULTY RATING:

YOU WILL NEED:
- A CALCULATOR (WELL, YOU WON'T NEED IT BUT YOUR FAMILY AND FRIENDS WILL!)
- PAPER
- A PEN OR PENCIL

What to do:

1

Make sure the person you are doing a trick on has some **money in their pocket**. Ask them to **count it and write down the amount** on a piece of paper, without telling you how much it is.

2

Ask them to **double the amount and write it down**.

£1.30 × 2 = £2.60

3 Ask them to **add 3 to the new total** and write down the figure again.

£1.30 × 2
= £2.60
+ 3 = £2.63

4 Ask them to **multiply that total by 5** (give them a calculator if they need it!) and tell them to write down the answer.

£1.30 × 2
= £2.60
+ 3 = £2.63
× 5 = £13.15

5 Then ask them to **subtract 6 from their total** and write down the final amount.

£1.30 × 2
= £2.60
+ 3 = £2.63
× 5 = £13.15
− 6 = £13.09

6 **Ask them for the final answer** they have written down, then **take off the last digit**, and you'll be able to work out how much the coins are worth instantly!

£1.30

Genius GUESSING

No doubt the **towering Trunchbull** would be horrified if you guessed her age and **humongous shoe size**! Master this mathematical trick and you can do just that!

DIFFICULTY RATING:

What to do:

1 Ask someone to **write down their age** on a piece of paper **without showing you**.

9

2 Tell them to **multiply it by 20** and write down the answer (give them a calculator if they need it!).

$9 \times 20 = 180$

3 Ask them to **add today's date to the total** (so if the date is the 3rd, they should add 3 to their total). Then they should write down that total.

$9 \times 20 = 180$
$180 + 3 = 183$

4 Next, ask them to **multiply the number by 5** and write down the answer.

$9 \times 20 = 180$
$180 + 3 = 183$
$183 \times 5 = 915$

5 Now ask them to **add their shoe size to the total** (if it's a half size, round it up to a whole number).

$$9 \times 20 = 180$$
$$180 + 3 = 183$$
$$183 \times 5 = 915$$
$$915 + 3 = 918$$

6 For the final result, ask them to **times the number of today's date by 5** and then **subtract that number from the total** they have written down.

$$9 \times 20 = 180$$
$$180 + 3 = 183$$
$$183 \times 5 = 915$$
$$915 + 3 = 918$$
$$3 \times 5 = 15$$
$$918 - 15 = 903$$

7 Ask them to show you their final answer **(but not the other numbers)**.

$$9 \quad 0 = 180$$
$$8 \times 5 = 9$$
$$9 \quad + 3 = \quad 8$$
$$3 \times 5 = 15$$
$$918 - 15 = \underline{903}$$

ANCIENT

The number you see can be **broken down** as follows – the **hundreds are the age** and the **remaining digits are the shoe size**. For example, if the number you see is **903**, the **age is 9**, which leaves **03**, so the **shoe size is 3**.

HUMONGOUS SHOE SIZE!

Always
BE A
WINNER!

To play this game you just need **two coins** and a **couple of unsuspecting grown-ups or friends** to get frustrated as you win every time!

 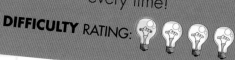
YOU WILL NEED:
- TWO COINS

What to do:

1 Ask your friend to toss **two coins**, but **not to show** you whether they are heads or tails. If they **both come up tails**, then ask them to toss the coins again.

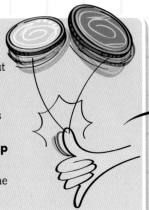

2 Ask your friend to show you **a coin that came up heads**, to prove that they did not both come up tails.

3 Tell your friend that you will guess what the **other, hidden coin is showing. If you get it right**, they must give you **10p. If you get it wrong**, you must give them **15p**.

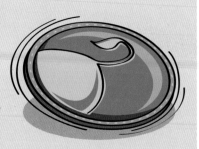

4

If you **always say "tails"**, you should win **two times out of three**! This is because the two coins can land in four different ways, as shown in the table here:

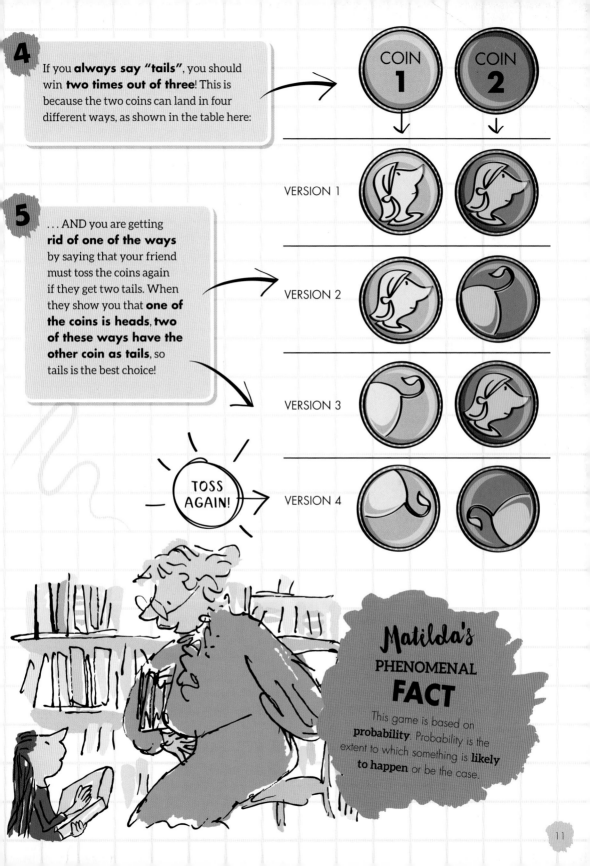

COIN **1**   COIN **2**

VERSION 1

5

...AND you are getting **rid of one of the ways** by saying that your friend must toss the coins again if they get two tails. When they show you that **one of the coins is heads**, **two of these ways have the other coin as tails**, so tails is the best choice!

VERSION 2

VERSION 3

TOSS AGAIN!

VERSION 4

Matilda's PHENOMENAL **FACT**

This game is based on **probability**. Probability is the extent to which something is **likely to happen** or be the case.

STAGGERING Sums

Even though **Mr Wormwood** doesn't believe her, Matilda really does have the **brainpower** to do **amazing arithmetic in her head**. Impress your grown-ups and friends by practising this clever big-number addition trick!

DIFFICULTY RATING:

YOU WILL NEED:
- A PENCIL
- A RULER
- SOME PAPER
- A CALCULATOR

What to do:

1

On a piece of paper **draw a grid with six rows and five columns**, with a **plus sign in the fifth row of the first column**, as shown. Then tell your friend that you are going to predict the result of a big addition sum!

COLUMNS

ROWS

+

2

Ask your friend to write a **four-digit number in the boxes at the top**, in columns two to five.

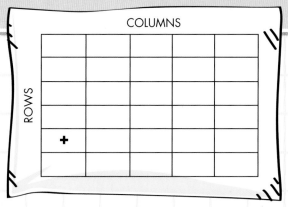

COLUMNS

	3	0	0	8
+				

ROWS

3

Subtract 2 from the number your friend wrote down – in this example, **3006** – put a 2 in front of it (**23006**), then write that number in the boxes in the last row of the table, saying that this is your **prediction for the result of the sum**.

		COLUMNS		
	3	0	0	8
+				
2	3	0	0	6

ROWS

4

Ask your friend to write **another four-digit number** underneath the original one.

		COLUMNS		
	3	0	0	8
	1	3	5	7
+				
2	3	0	0	6

ROWS

5

Now it's **your turn to write the next four-digit number** in the grid. Look at the second number written by your friend – **1357** – and **subtract each number from 9** to get the number you need to put in the grid.

(**For example:** you get **8642** from 9 – 1 = 8, 9 – 3 = 6, 9 – 5 = 4 and 9 – 7 = 2). The figure you put down, when added to your friend's number, must add up to **9999**.

		COLUMNS		
	3	0	0	8
	1	3	5	7
	8	6	4	2
+				
2	3	0	0	6

ROWS

6

Ask your friend to fill in another random **four-digit number** in the grid, then **repeat step 5** to work out what the last four-digit number should be and fill in the boxes.

Your sum is complete! Your prediction should be correct, but ask your friend to check the sum on a calculator and they'll be totally shocked you got it right!

		COLUMNS		
	3	0	0	8
	1	3	5	7
	8	6	4	2
	9	2	6	5
+	0	7	3	4
2	3	0	0	6

ROWS

Quick-THINKING TIPS

Use these tips to help you use maths for things in **everyday life**. Number one would help you add up Mr Wormwood's daily takings at his dodgy car dealership!

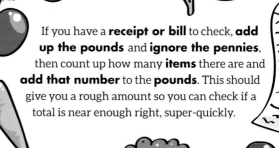

1

If you have a **receipt or bill** to check, **add up the pounds** and **ignore the pennies**, then count up how many **items** there are and **add that number** to the **pounds**. This should give you a rough amount so you can check if a total is near enough right, super-quickly.

2

If you are adding **5** to a number **greater than 5**, it's often easier to **take away 5** and **then add 10**.

3

To multiply a **two-digit** number by **11**, add the two digits together and put them in the middle.

72×11
$= 7 (7 + 2 = 9) 2$
$= 792$

What if the two numbers add up to **more than 10**? There's a similar trick for that too. Can you work out what it is?

TOP **TIP** **Practise sums whenever you can.** The more you do, the easier they get and the more you can use maths to your advantage against unsuspecting grown-ups!

14

CHAPTER TWO
PUZZLING
PAPER

PUZZLING PAPER

When **Miss Honey** meets **Matilda** for the first time, she is full of wonder about the **extraordinary child**. But when she sees Matilda move a glass with just her eyes, she is **utterly** amazed . . .

Miss Honey's mouth **DROPPED** open and her eyes **stretched** so wide you could see the whites all round. She didn't say a word. She couldn't. The shock of seeing the miracle performed had STRUCK HER DUMB.

Miss Honey was still gazing at the child in ABSOLUTE WONDERMENT, as though she were **THE CREATION**, THE BEGINNING OF THE WORLD, THE FIRST MORNING.

'IT'S NOT POSSIBLE!'

Miss Honey was gasping. 'I don't believe it! I simply don't believe it!'

'Am I a **PHENOMENON**?' Matilda asked.

'It is quite possible that you are,' Miss Honey said.

Inspired by Matilda's **ASTOUNDING IMAGINATION**, this chapter is all about **PHENOMENAL** things you can do with not much more than some bits of **PAPER** and your remarkable self! They include:

Cutting a piece of paper big enough to **walk through**!

Making a **perpetual paper spinner**!

Performing **loopy paper tricks**!

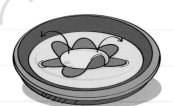

Creating **paper flowers** that bloom by themselves!

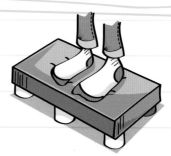

And even making your own **super-strong paper platform**!

Mind–SPINNING BRILLIANCE

YOU WILL NEED:
- A PIECE OF A4 PAPER
- A PENCIL WITH AN ERASER AT ONE END
- SCISSORS
- A LONG PIN OR NEEDLE
- STICKY TAPE
- A THIMBLE
- A LAMP WITH A LAMPSHADE

Matilda made Miss Honey's **head spin** with how **marvellously clever** she was. Now it's your turn to do the same, with this **perpetual paper spinner**! Get ready to astound . . .

DIFFICULTY RATING:

What to do:

1

Draw a spiral shape on your piece of paper, as shown.

2

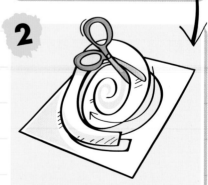

Cut along **the line of the spiral** to make a **snake shape**.

3

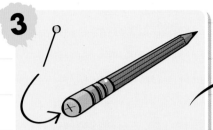

Ask a **grown-up** to help **push the pin into the eraser** on the end of the pencil.

4

Use **sticky tape** to **attach** the **thimble underneath** the **centre** of your paper spiral.

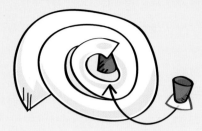

5

Stick your **pencil** securely to the **top of the lampshade** with sticky tape, so that the pin is at the top.

6

Slot the **spiral over the pencil**, using the thimble to balance it on top of the pin.

Matilda's
PHENOMENAL
FACT

As the **air around the lamp heats up**, your paper spiral **spins**. This is because **hot air** is **less dense** than cold air. The air that is around the lamp rises **upwards** and **pushes on the spiral**, making it **turn**! As long as the hot air continues to do this, your spiral should continue to spin round and round.

7 **Switch on** the lamp and watch it **spin**!

Blooming MAGICAL!

YOU WILL NEED:
- THIN PAPER
- COLOURED PENCILS OR CRAYONS
- SCISSORS
- A SHALLOW BOWL
- WATER

When Matilda first tells Miss Honey about her **powers**, her teacher thinks it's just her imagination, and needs convincing. Now it's your turn **to convince grown-ups of your brilliance** . . .
Try this clever trick to show them that you can make **paper come to life**!

DIFFICULTY RATING:

What to do:

1

Draw a flower with distinct petal shapes on your paper, colour it in and **cut it out**.

2

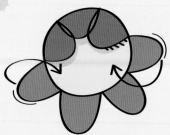

Fold all the petals of your flower into the **centre**, one by one.

3

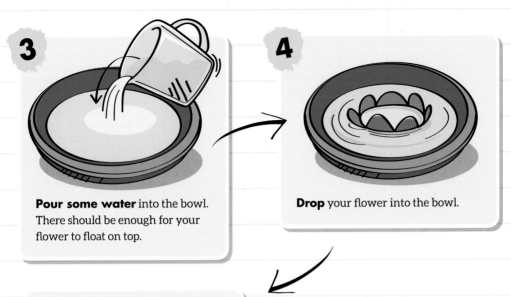

Pour some water into the bowl. There should be enough for your flower to float on top.

4

Drop your flower into the bowl.

5 Your audience will be amazed to see your flower blossom and **open up**!

Matilda's
PHENOMENAL
FACT

As paper is made from plant materials, it **absorbs water quickly**. The water makes the paper **swell up** and push the petals **up and out**.

LOOP-tastic!

YOU WILL NEED:
- PAPER — CUT INTO TWO STRIPS ABOUT 4CM WIDE AND 20CM LONG
- SCISSORS
- STICKY TAPE
- A PENCIL

As you have already seen in the first chapter, having an incredible knowledge of **mathematics** like Matilda helps you to understand many amazing things! Now it's time to **combine your maths and your paper skills** to create a **loopy trick** . . . as if by magic!

DIFFICULTY RATING:

What to do:

1

Take one end of one of the strips and **twist it over once**, sticky taping the ends together.

2

Use a pencil to **draw a line** along the **middle of the strip**, going all the way round.

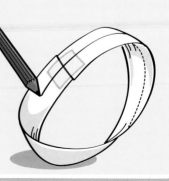

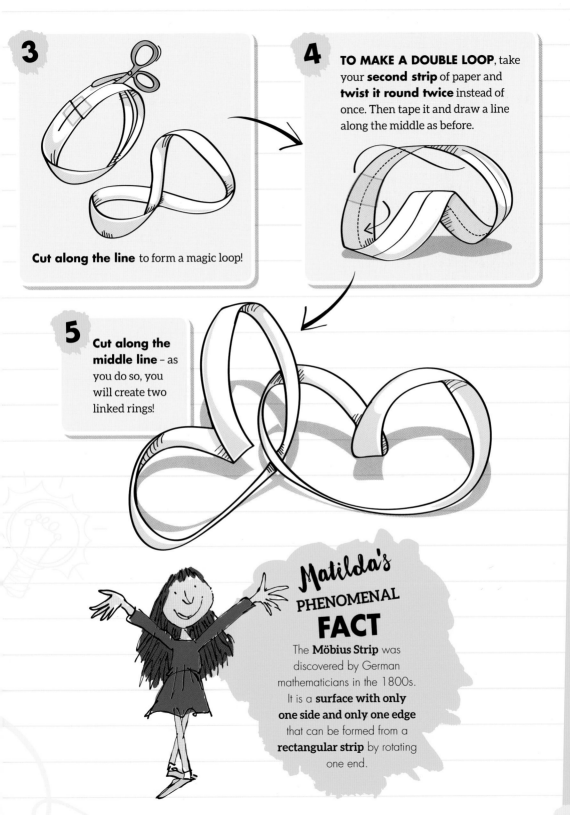

3

Cut along the line to form a magic loop!

4

TO MAKE A DOUBLE LOOP, take your **second strip** of paper and **twist it round twice** instead of once. Then tape it and draw a line along the middle as before.

5

Cut along the middle line – as you do so, you will create two linked rings!

Matilda's PHENOMENAL **FACT**

The **Möbius Strip** was discovered by German mathematicians in the 1800s. It is a **surface with only one side and only one edge** that can be formed from a **rectangular strip** by rotating one end.

SUPER-STRONG PAPER

YOU WILL NEED:
- A LARGE PIECE OF PAPER AROUND A3 IN SIZE
- A PEN
- SCISSORS
- STICKY TAPE
- A CARDBOARD BOX LID

It's time to make some paper appear to be so **super strong** that even the mighty Trunchbull couldn't tear it in two!

DIFFICULTY RATING:

What to do:

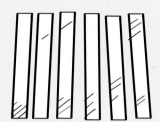

1

Cut your piece of paper into **six equal-sized strips**.

2

One at a time, wrap each strip of paper **tightly around two of your fingers** and tape together once you have a **cylinder**.

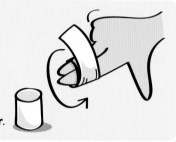

3

Line up your paper cylinders to make a **rectangular base**, as shown, and place an **upturned cardboard box lid** on top of the paper cylinders.

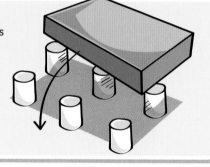

4

Try standing on top – does the paper hold your weight? If it doesn't hold you, then repeat the experiment with some heavy objects that will impress your friends and family. You could also try making a few more paper cylinders to see if that holds even more weight.

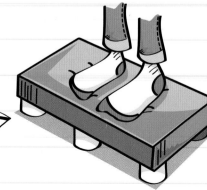

(**DISCLAIMER**: It's possible that no paper in the world is strong enough to hold the Trunchbull, so don't ask her to have a go. In fact, just steer clear and don't ask her anything.)

IMPOSSI-PAPER

Follow these steps and see how many times you can **fold a piece of paper in half**. It's not as easy as you'd think!

DIFFICULTY RATING: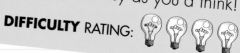

YOU WILL NEED:

- LOTS OF DIFFERENT-SIZED PIECES OF PAPER
- YOUR HANDS
- A RULER TO HELP YOU FOLD

What to do:

EXPERIMENT! Try folding each piece of paper in half again and again! How many times can you fold each one? Fill in your results on the table below.

SIZE OF PAPER	NUMBER OF FOLDS

DARING DEED
Challenge a grown-up to fold a piece of paper in half **more than eight times** (without telling them how difficult it is!).

PAPER *Ball*

This is a **brilliant ball** made of card and lots of **five-sided shapes** called **pentagons**, so Matilda's mathematical mind would be suitably impressed! It's also a rather wonderful word. Get ready to make . . . a **dodecahedron ball**!

DIFFICULTY RATING:

YOU WILL NEED:

- A4 PIECE OF CARD
- A PENCIL
- SCISSORS
- GLUE

What to do:

1

Trace the shape opposite on to the piece of card, then cut it out.

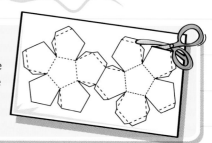

2

Fold the **dotted lines** in the centre up and then **open them out**.

3

Fold the **dashed lines** of the grey tabs over.

4

Place one of the **centre pentagon shapes** down on a table, then fold the dotted lines up and **'cup'** the ball together, as shown.

5 **Glue the tabs** to secure the shape.

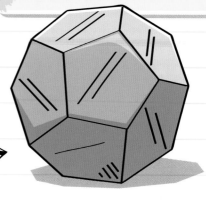

Matilda's
PHENOMENAL
FACT
A dodecahedron
has **12 faces, 20 corners**
and **30 edges**!

WALK-THROUGH *Wonder*

YOU WILL NEED:
- A PIECE OF A4 PAPER
- SCISSORS

Remember how the Trunchbull flung a boy **'clear out of the classroom window'**? Well, we're not going to learn how to do that – sorry. Instead, follow the steps to make a **window** from a **small piece of paper**, and **step through it**. It's still impressive, but rather less violent.

DIFFICULTY RATING:

What to do:

1 **Show** your piece of paper to your audience and **tell them** you are going to walk through it!

2 **Fold** the piece of paper in half **lengthwise**.

3 Cut the paper **horizontally from the fold upwards**, but **NOT all the way to the top** – leave about **2cm**, as shown.

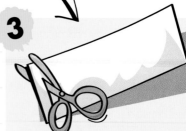

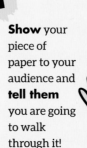

4

Now **turn the paper round** and cut towards the fold, but **NOT all the way to the top**, leaving **2cm** again.

5

Keep making cuts in the paper, as shown, **alternating sides**. Make sure that you **finish with a cut from the fold upwards**, as with your first cut.

6

Cut through the folded parts of the paper **EXCEPT for the first and last folds**, as shown.

7

Unfold the paper to find a very large window for you to walk through. Walk through it and say, **'Ta-da!'**

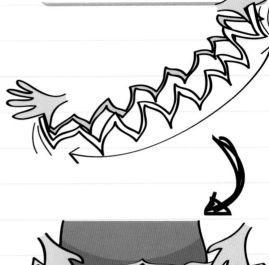

GIRL POWER!

Follow these steps and impress everyone by **drawing a girl** out of the word **'girl'**.

DIFFICULTY RATING: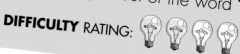

YOU WILL NEED:
- A PIECE OF A4 PAPER
- A PENCIL

What to do:

1. girl

2. girl

3. girl

4.

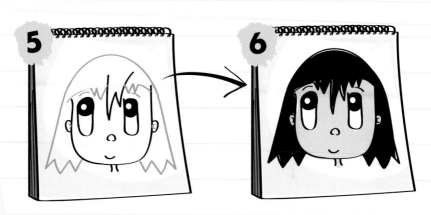

5.

6.

CHAPTER THREE

SIMPLY
SUPERNATURAL
Science

SIMPLY SUPERNATURAL *Science*

When Matilda tells her teacher that she has the power to **make objects move with her mind**, Miss Honey doesn't believe her – but she is soon convinced by a demonstration of Matilda's amazing abilities!

'I am still not following you,' Miss Honey said. 'Do you mean you actually **WILLED** the glass to tip over?'

'YES,' Matilda said. 'WITH MY EYES.'

Miss Honey was silent for a moment. She did not think Matilda was meaning to tell a lie. It was more likely that she was simply allowing her VIVID IMAGINATION to run away with her. 'You mean you were sitting where you are now and you **TOLD THE GLASS TO TOPPLE OVER** and it did?'

'Something like that, Miss Honey, **YES**.'

32

Inspired by Matilda's mighty ability to make objects move, the activities in this chapter will make you seem **supernaturally powerful**! They all have a **scientific twist**, and use basic principles to do amazing things:

Poke a skewer through a balloon without popping it!

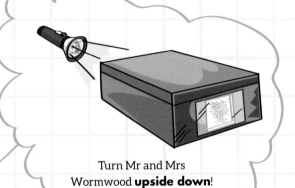

Turn Mr and Mrs Wormwood **upside down**!

Trap the Trunchbull in a cage!

Actually **bend water**!

Grow a **funny wig** for Mr Wormwood!

Make things **levitate** and **move on their own**!

Balloon TRICK

Make the impossible seem possible just like Matilda, by **poking a sharp point right through a balloon** without it popping! Challenge your audience to poke skewers through the balloons and watch them go **pop**! Then show them how it's really done . . .

DIFFICULTY RATING:

YOU WILL NEED:
- SOME ROUND (NOT LONG) BALLOONS
- SOME SHARP WOODEN KEBAB SKEWERS ⚠

What to do:

1

Blow up some balloons so they are **not fully inflated** and knot the ends.

2 Take a balloon and **find the dark patch on the top** (the opposite end to your knot). **Gently push the skewer** through the dark patch, **twisting it** as you do so.

3 When the skewer reaches the other end of the balloon, **push it gently through** the soft part next to the knot, using the **same twisting motion**.

Ta-da! The sharp skewer has gone through the balloon **without popping it**!

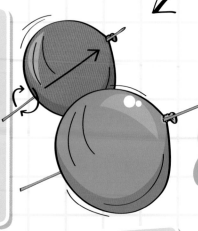

Matilda's PHENOMENAL FACT

At the points with **low tension** (the top and bottom of the balloon), you can create a small hole without **breaking the whole surface** of the balloon and making it pop!

TOP TIP If you follow the steps and still pop the balloon, just **keep practising** – it will work!

Pencil TRICK

Stun your audience again by **poking a pencil through a bag of water** without spilling a drop!

DIFFICULTY RATING: 💡💡💡💡

YOU WILL NEED:
- A SMALL ZIPLOCK PLASTIC BAG
- WATER
- A SHARP PENCIL

What to do:

1 Pour water into your plastic bag until it is about **¾ full and zip it shut**.

2 Hold the bag with one hand, and use the other to push the pencil through **one side of the bag to the other**.

Matilda's
PHENOMENAL
FACT

Ziplock bags are made of a **polymer**. Polymers have **long chains of flexible molecules**. When you poke the pencil through, it **slides between the chains** of molecules. The molecule chains then make **a seal around the pencil**, stopping the water from escaping! Clever stuff!

3 **Ta-da!** No water should spill! If you like, you can try **poking more pencils** through your bag!

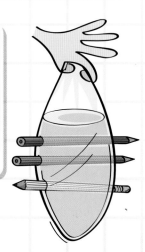

FLOATING FEAT

When Miss Trunchbull wrongly accuses her of putting a **newt** in the water jug, **Matilda** feels a strange sense of power. She uses that power to **tip over a water glass** without touching it and spill it on her **horrible head teacher**! From that moment on Matilda isn't frightened . . . not even of the **terrifying Trunchbull**.

DIFFICULTY RATING:

What to do:

1 Use tissue paper and a pen to **trace over the newt shown above twice**, then cut them out.

2 Blow up the balloon and **rub it** with the jumper or fake fur for **at least 20 seconds**.

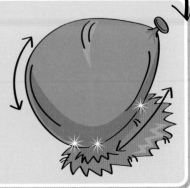

3

Hold the balloon **near your hair**. If you **feel your hair moving towards it**, then the balloon is ready!

4

Hold the balloon **above** the newts. Command, **'Lift up! Lift up!'** and amaze your audience as the newts float up without you touching them!

Matilda's
PHENOMENAL
FACT

While performing this trick, you discovered **static electricity – a stationary electric charge produced by friction** (when two objects rub together). When you rubbed the balloon, **electrons jumped from the material onto it**. These **electrons produced the force** that pulled on the paper newts, lifting them up!

TOP TIP

Use the **same process** to lift up feathers and polystyrene balls.

TRAP *the* TRUNCHBULL

Find out how your **brain can trick your eyes** by trapping the wicked Trunchbull in a cage. (If only it was real!)

DIFFICULTY RATING:

YOU WILL NEED:
- A PHOTOCOPIER OR A PIECE OF PAPER AND A PEN FOR COPYING MISS TRUNCHBULL AND THE CAGE
- SCISSORS
- GLUE DOTS
- A COCKTAIL STICK

What to do:

1

Photocopy or **copy** the pictures of Miss Trunchbull and the cage on to a piece of paper and cut them out, making sure that the shape around Miss Trunchbull is the **same size** as the cage.

2

Turn the cage over and stick the glue dots on the back.

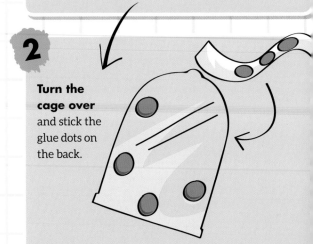

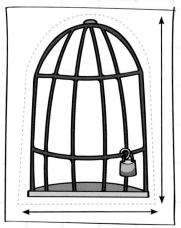

3

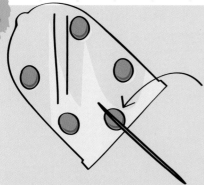

Place **the end** of the cocktail stick on the **cage's bottom glue dot**.

4

Stick another glue dot **on top of the cocktail stick**, then place the picture of Miss Trunchbull **on top** of all the glue dots.

5

Hold up the stick between your **forefinger and thumb**, then say the words, 'It's time to put the Trunchbull where she belongs . . . in a cage!' Rub your finger and thumb **back and forth to spin the stick** very quickly. Soon Miss Trunchbull will appear to be locked in the cage!

Matilda's
PHENOMENAL
FACT

How does this illusion work?
Well, as the pictures on the stick spin to and fro, your eyes see one picture after the other. When they **move really quickly, your brain cannot separate them**, so you just see one picture of Miss Trunchbull in the cage!

Bendy WATER

This is an **incredibly simple yet powerful trick** to have up your sleeve when you need to show a grown-up that you're definitely no witless weed! First, tell them that you can make **water bend** without even touching it, then follow these steps.

DIFFICULTY RATING:

YOU WILL NEED:
- A RUNNING TAP
- A HAIR COMB

1 Turn on your **cold tap** so that a **steady stream** of water comes out.

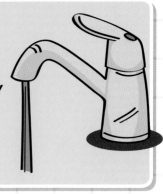

2 **Comb** through your hair **ten times**.

3 Put the **comb near the water** and watch it bend!

Matilda's PHENOMENAL FACT

This trick is down to **static electricity** – like the levitating trick on pages 36–37. The **negatively charged comb repels the electrons in the water**, so the water near the comb then has a positive charge. The attraction between this charge and the comb's negative one creates a net force on the water, **making it bend**!

INSTANT Ice

Another **quick and simple** way to astound others with your extraordinary powers is by **turning water into ice** as you pour it!

DIFFICULTY RATING:

YOU WILL NEED:
- 1 LITRE BOTTLE OF FILTERED WATER
- A BUCKET
- 4KG ICE CUBES
- 1.5KG TABLE SALT
- A CLEAR MIXING BOWL

What to do:

1 Put your bottle of water **into a bucket** and pack **3kg** of the ice cubes **around the base**. Pour **1.5kg salt over the ice** and top the bucket up with **cold tap water**.

2 **Leave the bottle** – don't touch it for around **30 minutes**. If you have a thermometer, you can carefully check the water around the bottle – it should reach **–8°C**.

3 Making sure that its contents are **still liquid, carefully** take the bottle out of its bucket. Put the **remaining ice cubes** into the clear mixing bowl.

4 **Unscrew** the bottle, **pour** the filtered water on to the ice cubes – and watch it instantly **turn to ice**!

TOPSY-TURVY
WORMWOODS

Help Matilda get **revenge** on her mean parents – and turn their whole world **upside down** by making a **pinhole projector**!

DIFFICULTY RATING: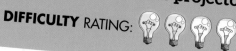

What to do:

1

Make a hole in the **centre of one end of your shoebox** by **piercing** it with a drawing pin, then **widening the hole** with a pencil.

2

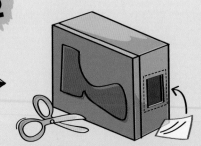

Cut out a small rectangle shape in the **other end of the shoebox**, then cut out and tape a piece of **greaseproof paper to cover it**. This will be the window you look through.

3

Get your torch and cut out a piece of greaseproof paper **big enough to cover the bulb end**.

4

On the paper, **trace the outline** of Mr Wormwood on the opposite page with your black felt-tip, then colour him in **dark blue or green**. Stick this over the bulb end of your torch.

5

Go into a **dark room**. Place your torch on a table and switch it on.

6

Pick up your projector box, then **stand about a metre away from the torch, pointing the pinhole at the light**. Look through the window. What happens to Mr Wormwood?

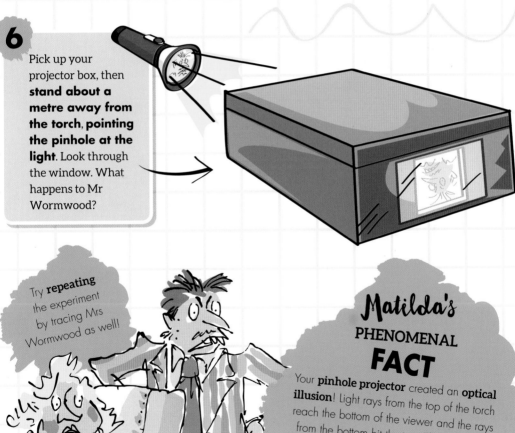

Try **repeating** the experiment by tracing Mrs Wormwood as well!

Matilda's
PHENOMENAL
FACT

Your **pinhole projector** created an **optical illusion**! Light rays from the top of the torch reach the bottom of the viewer and the rays from the bottom hit the top. The **two rays cross over** as they pass through the hole you made, so that you see **Mr and Mrs Wormwood upside down**!

COLOUR Explosion

When **Matilda** sought revenge on her parents, she used anything she could get her hands on to do her tricks! Try this trick using just **milk**, **washing-up liquid** and **food colouring**.

DIFFICULTY RATING: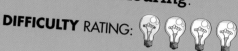

YOU WILL NEED:

- MILK
- A TRAY
- FOOD COLOURING (A FEW DIFFERENT COLOURS)
- A COTTON BUD
- WASHING-UP LIQUID
- WATERCOLOUR PAPER

What to do:

1

Tip enough **milk** into the tray to **cover the bottom**, then **add** your food colouring.

2

Dip the cotton bud in the washing-up liquid and **stir** it into the milk. The colours should **spread out and swirl around**.

3

When you're happy with the colourful **'picture'**, lay your watercolour paper on the **surface of the milk**, **pressing down lightly**, then **quickly lift it up** and **turn it over to dry**.

A Wig FOR WORMWOOD

After Matilda's **foul father** calls her a cheat and a liar, she tricks him into turning his hair platinum blond using Mrs Wormwood's hair dye! Try this experiment to grow your own **funny hair** for Mr Wormwood!

DIFFICULTY RATING: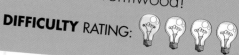

YOU WILL NEED:

- 10 PIECES OF KITCHEN TOWEL
- A PLATE
- A SPOON
- CRESS SEEDS
- WATER

What to do:

1 Lay the **pieces of kitchen towel** on the plate, then spoon water on to **soak** them.

2 **Sprinkle cress seeds** into the shape you would like for your wig.

3 Place the plate near a window. Use a **spoon to pour water** onto the kitchen towel **around your seeds** each day.

4 **After a week** your wig will have grown!

CHAPTER FOUR
FANTASTIC
Food

FANTASTIC *Food*

Meet brave **Bruce Bogtrotter**, the boy who dared to take a slice of **Miss Trunchbull's special chocolate cake** and lived to eat again!

'You do not leave this platform and nobody leaves this hall until you have **EATEN THE ENTIRE CAKE** that is sitting there in front of you! Do I make myself clear, **BOGTROTTER**?'

Very **SLOWLY** the boy cut himself another slice and began to eat it . . . he kept **PUSHING** the stuff into his mouth with the dogged perseverance of a long-distance runner who has sighted the finishing-line and knows he must keep going.

As the very last mouthful disappeared, a **TREMENDOUS CHEER** rose up from the audience and children were leaping on to their chairs and **YELLING** and **CLAPPING** and **SHOUTING**, 'Well done, Brucie! Good for you, Brucie!'

'GO TO BLAZES!' screamed the Trunchbull.

As a celebration of Bruce's incredible **triumph over the Trunchbull**, this chapter is full to bursting with **mischievous tricks** you can do with **food**, including:

Placing a **packet of ketchup in a bottle of water** and making it rise and fall on your command.

Making an egg that's **unbreakable**.

Peeling a banana to reveal that it's **already been sliced**.

Making a coffee cup **float in the air**.

And, most thrillingly of all, imagining Miss Trunchbull's face as you **EXPLODE a chocolate cake**!

CONTROLLING
Ketchup
MIRACLE!

This trick is inspired by Matilda's **amazing ability** to make things move at **her command**. It's time for you to use your own **incredible powers** to make a ketchup packet rise and fall!

DIFFICULTY RATING:

What to do:

1

Drop the packet of ketchup **into the bottle**.

2

Fill the bottle with water and **screw on the lid**.

3

The ketchup packet should **float in the middle of the bottle**.

4

Squeeze the bottle and say the words, 'I command you to sink!' and the packet should sink.

5

Pretend you are concentrating hard and using your incredible powers, then say the words, 'I command you to float!' as you **relax your grip on the bottle** and make the packet float up again!

Matilda's PHENOMENAL FACT

There is an **air bubble trapped** inside the ketchup packet, which makes it float. When you squeeze the bottle, the bubble is made smaller. The packet is smaller but its **mass is still the same**, so squeezing the bottle **increases the density** of the packet. When the packet is **denser than the water**, the packet will sink. When you relax your grip, **you release the pressure**, so the **air bubble expands** and the packet rises again.

TOP TIP

If your ketchup packet sinks at first, try another packet, or remove the water and ketchup from the bottle, then **bend the packet slightly** and try again.

ORANGE DROP

Here's another chance to prove that you can **move things without touching them**, like Matilda.

DIFFICULTY RATING:

YOU WILL NEED:

- A PIECE OF CARD ABOUT 10CM X 8CM
- STICKY TAPE
- A POSTCARD
- A MUG
- A SMALL ORANGE

What to do:

1 **Fold** your piece of card into a **rectangular column**, as shown, and **tape it together**.

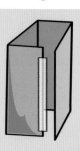

2

Place the postcard on the mug and **balance** the column on top.

3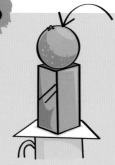

Ask a grown-up or friend to **balance a small orange** on top of your column so that it is **above the mug**.

Matilda's PHENOMENAL FACT

As the **orange is heavier than the column**, it does not move as easily, so it goes straight down. This is called **inertia**. Inertia is **how hard it is for a force to move an object**. The column has low inertia, but the orange has high inertia.

4 Say the words, **'Ta-da, no hands!'** as you tug the postcard away quickly, making your column fall to the side, and the orange drop into the mug!

GO Bananas TRICK

Now make your audience **go bananas** with this mischievous trick!

DIFFICULTY RATING:

What to do:

YOU WILL NEED:
- A BANANA
- A NEEDLE
- A TEA TOWEL

1 **Before** you perform your trick, push the needle into the banana in a spot that **isn't too noticeable**. Then **wiggle it to and fro** to create a cut across the banana inside, keeping the hole as small as possible.

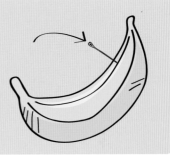

2 Push the needle into the banana at **another spot** and repeat the wiggling motion. Repeat this to make as many cuts as you like. You should only be able to see tiny holes **in a line** along the banana.

3 **Now it's time for the trick!** Show the banana to the audience so that they can see it is whole and not sliced.

4 **Cover** the banana with the tea towel, then say, **'Slice, banana, slice!'**

Take the tea towel away, then **peel the banana** to reveal the slices!

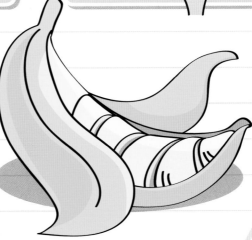

53

BOUNCY Egg

Even if your parents aren't as dim as Matilda's, you can try these fun **EGGS-periments** on them and they're bound to be **EGGS-tremely** amused!

DIFFICULTY RATING:

YOU WILL NEED:
- A HARD-BOILED EGG
- A LARGE BOWL
- WHITE VINEGAR
- WATER

TOP TIP
You need to prepare this trick **three days before** you want to perform it!

What to do:

1
Put your hard-boiled egg in the bowl and **completely cover it with vinegar**. Then leave it for three days.

2
After three days, remove the egg from the bowl and **rinse the shell away** with water (it should have dissolved).

3
The egg should **feel rubbery** and you should be able to bounce it. **Test it before you perform** your trick, then amaze your audience with your bouncing egg!

Matilda's PHENOMENAL FACT

The shell of an egg is made of **calcium carbonate** and **vinegar is acetic acid**, and the two react together. The eggshell dissolves, but the **membrane inside** it remains intact, making it feel rubbery.

UNBREAKABLE Egg

 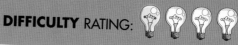

YOU WILL NEED:
- AN EGG
- CLING FILM

What to do:

1

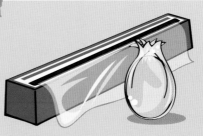

Wrap the egg in cling film.

2

Put the wrapped egg in the **centre of your palm** and close your hand around it so your fingers are **completely wrapped around the egg**, then squeeze it very hard.

3

The egg should remain in **one piece!**

Matilda's PHENOMENAL FACT

Eggshells are fragile, especially when you drop them! But the **shape of an egg is very strong**, so if pressure is applied **evenly all over the shell**, it won't break!

DIY COOKER

What to do:

YOU WILL NEED:
- A SUNNY DAY!
- ADHESIVE PUTTY
- A LARGE BOWL
- KITCHEN FOIL
- A LARGE MARSHMALLOW
- A COCKTAIL STICK
- CLING FILM
- STONES

1 Use the kitchen foil to **line the bowl** and stick a bit of putty in the **centre**.

2 Stick a marshmallow on **one end of a cocktail stick** and push the **other end** into the putty so that it is **standing upright**.

Given the **utterly revolting** and greasy meals Matilda's parents serve up, she should probably have tried to find an ingenious way to feed herself. Follow the steps to make your very own **DIY cooker**!

DIFFICULTY RATING:

3

Use the cling film to cover the **top of the bowl**, then place it outside in a **sunny spot**.

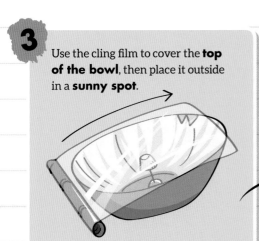

4

Using stones to support the bowl at an **angle**, position it so that the marshmallow is **facing the sun** and leave it for about **15 minutes**.

5

Ask a grown-up to help you check on your marshmallow – it should have started to melt. You have made your own cooker! If it hasn't melted, cover and leave it for another 15 minutes. Careful, as it will be hot!

Matilda's
PHENOMENAL
FACT

The **key things** here for your cooker are the **cling film** and the **foil**. The cling film lets the sunlight into the bowl and **traps the heat**. The foil **reflects the light and heat** around the bowl and on to the marshmallow, cooking it.

COLOUR-CHANGING
Soda TRICK

Matilda's **brave friend** Lavender had the job of filling the Trunchbull's jug of water, and that gave her the perfect opportunity to put a slimy newt in it! **Tamper with your drinks** at home as you perform this sneaky trick!

DIFFICULTY RATING:

What to do:

1 **Tear** the red cabbage leaves into **small pieces** and put them in a bowl.

2 **Ask a grown-up** to pour boiling water over the cabbage until it is **covered**, then leave it to **cool completely**.

3 Pour through a **sieve** into another bowl (you can discard the cabbage leaves).

4 **Pour** the liquid from the bowl into a jug and **stir** in the bicarbonate of soda. The liquid should turn **bright blue** (if it doesn't, stir in some more bicarbonate of soda).

5 Put the jug in the fridge for about **30 minutes**.

6 **It's now time to perform your trick!** Put a glass on a table and take your jug out of the fridge. Pour lemonade into the glass.

7 Say your command – **'Change colour now!'** – as you pour a small amount of the blue liquid into the glass. The lemonade won't turn blue, but will turn into **purple lemonade**! Now pour some more!

EXPLODING
Chocolate
CAKE

Take your **revenge** on the terrible Trunchbull by making her favourite chocolate cake . . . . **explode!**

DIFFICULTY RATING:

YOU WILL NEED:
Equipment
- A ROUND CAKE CUTTER BIG ENOUGH TO GO AROUND YOUR PLASTIC BOTTLE, PLUS SOME SMALLER ONES
- A TRAY
- A BUTTER KNIFE
- A CLEAN 330ML PLASTIC BOTTLE
- A ROLLING PIN
- A BOWL
- A PASTRY BRUSH
- A JUG
- A SPOON (FOR MIXING)

Ingredients
- 3 PLAIN ROUND SPONGE CAKES (BOUGHT OR HOME MADE)
- 2 TUBS OF BUTTERCREAM
- READY-TO-ROLL MARZIPAN
- 200G COOKING CHOCOLATE
- A GROWN-UP TO MELT IT
- RED FOOD COLOURING
- 330ML DIET COLA
- A PACKET OF SOFT MINTS
- COLOURED SPRINKLES

What to do:

1

Use the cake cutter to **cut a hole** in the **middle** of one of the sponge cakes, then place the cake on a tray.

2

Spread buttercream over the **top of the sponge ring**.

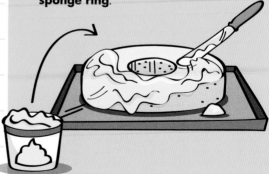

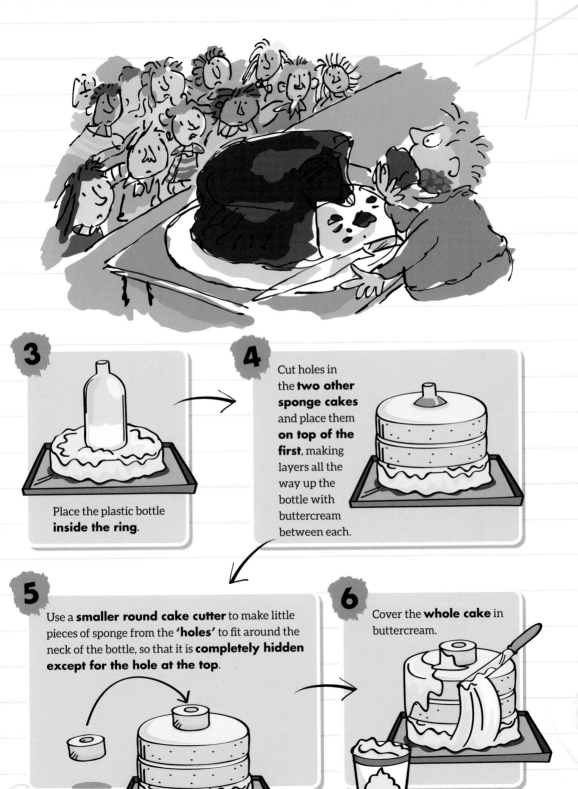

3

Place the plastic bottle **inside the ring**.

4

Cut holes in the **two other sponge cakes** and place them **on top of the first**, making layers all the way up the bottle with buttercream between each.

5

Use a **smaller round cake cutter** to make little pieces of sponge from the **'holes'** to fit around the neck of the bottle, so that it is **completely hidden except for the hole at the top**.

6

Cover the **whole cake** in buttercream.

7
With your rolling pin, roll a sheet of marzipan out into a **big circle**, then **cover the cake** with it.

8
Make a **hole at the top** where the bottle opening is.

9
Ask a grown-up to melt your bar of cooking chocolate and put it in a bowl, then use the pastry brush to **brush** the chocolate over the **whole cake**. You can decorate it with sprinkles too, if you like. Then leave the chocolate icing to **set**.

10 **Explosion time!** When you are ready to give the cake to the person you want to surprise, follow these next steps. **Drop** a **little bit** of red food colouring into a jug, then **gradually add the cola**, mixing them together **gently** as you go. Make sure you've got the **right amount to fit in the plastic bottle** inside the cake.

11 Pour the **cola and food colouring** into the bottle in your cake.

12 Make sure that the unsuspecting grown-up you are tricking is **standing right by the cake**. Then count down, **'Five, four, three, two, one . . .'** and **drop the mints** into the bottle as **quickly** as you can . . .

FAST FOODIE *Illusion* TRICK

Cook up a **quick trick** to play on unsuspecting people at home.

DIFFICULTY RATING:

YOU WILL NEED:
- STICKY TAPE
- A TIN MUG

What to do:

1 Attach a **loop** of clear sticky tape to the **side of the mug**. Then, when you are ready to perform your trick, hold the empty mug with **both hands**.

2 **Face your audience** and tell them that you are going to try and make the mug float in mid-air.

3 Press **one thumb against** the sticky tape. Then **gradually open up both hands** at the same time and, while you do this, push them **slightly forward** as if you're following the floating mug.

CHAPTER FIVE
MISCHIEVOUS
MESSAGES

MISCHIEVOUS
MESSAGES

When Matilda hears how **terribly cruel** Miss Trunchbu[ll] has been to gentle Miss Honey, she conjures up the **ultimate revenge** against tha[t] foul and **fiery dragon**!

'WHAT THE **BLAZES** IS THIS?'

yelled the Trunchbull. It had shaken her to see her own

first name being written like that by an invisible hand . . .

'WHO'S **DOING** THIS?'

> Agatha, this is Magnus
> Agatha, give my Jenny
> back her house
> Then get out of here.
> If you don't, I will come
> and get you . . .

The woman's face had turned
WHITE AS SNOW . . .

And there she was, the **HUGE** figure of the Headmistress, stretched FULL-LENGTH on her back across the floor, out for the count.

Feeling **secretive** and **rebellious**? This chapter is inspired by Matilda's mischievous, miraculous **MESSAGE WRITING**, and includes all you need to know for:

Writing **secret invisible messages**!

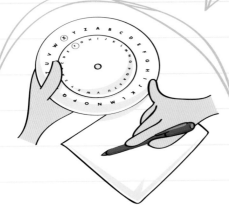

Building clever **coding wheels**!

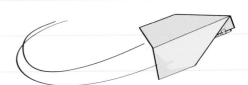

Flying **hidden messages** to your friends!

Making up **riddles** and **limericks**!

Using **clever word tricks** and **games** to bamboozle the socks off your friends and family!

INK-REDIBLE INVISIBLE Ink

You may not be able to make a **piece of chalk** write on its own like Matilda, but there are lots of clever ways to make messages appear as if by **magic**!

YOU WILL NEED:

- A BOWL
- HALF A LEMON
- A SPOON
- WATER
- COTTON BUD/FEATHER QUILL PEN/TOOTHPICK OR TOOTHBRUSH TO WRITE WITH
- SHEETS OF WHITE PAPER
- A HEAT SOURCE LIKE SUNLIGHT OR A LIGHT BULB THAT YOU CAN HOLD PAPER CLOSE TO
- SALT
- A WAX CRAYON

What to do:

1

Squeeze some lemon juice into the bowl and **stir** in a few drops of water with a spoon.

2

Dip your quill pen or cotton bud into the juice and write a message on a piece of paper.

3

Give your message to a friend and tell them to **heat it in sunlight**, or by asking a **grown-up** to hold it close to a light bulb.

LOOK NO *Ink?*

If all you have to hand is paper and pencils, you can still write mischievous messages! Simply take **two pieces of paper** and lay one over the other. Write your message on the top piece, **pressing down very hard**. Remove this top sheet and destroy it, then **pass the bottom sheet** to a friend.

They must **shade over the piece of paper** with a soft pencil to make the message magically appear – when no one is looking, of course!

TOP **TIP**

If you can't heat the paper, you can try **putting salt on the drying juice**, leaving it for one minute, then **wiping the salt away**. Then ask your friend to colour over the message with a **wax crayon** to reveal it.

SUPER **SIMPLE** MISCHIEVOUS *Messages*

Matilda's PHENOMENAL **FACT**

Diluting the lemon juice with water makes it very tricky to see, but **when it's heated**, the juice **oxidizes and turns brown** to reveal the message. You can also try using other liquids like orange juice, milk, honey and vinegar.

If you don't have much time but do have a **white crayon** to hand, you can use it to write a message on **white paper**. Ask a friend to **paint over it** with watercolour paint to reveal what it says!

SECRET *Code* WHEELS

Another way to get secret messages to friends and comrades is by **writing in code**. Follow the instructions to make a **code wheel** and send **top-secret messages**. Just make sure the wheel never ends up in the hands of your enemy – especially not those of the terrifying Trunchbull or any other foul grown-ups . . .

DIFFICULTY RATING:

YOU WILL NEED:
- TRACING PAPER AND NORMAL PAPER
- A PEN
- SCISSORS
- A SPLIT-PIN PAPER FASTENER

What to do:

1

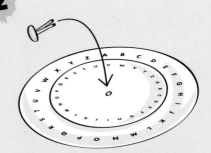

Photocopy or trace the two circles opposite onto a piece of paper and **cut them out**.

2

Put the small circle **on top** of the larger one so that their **centre points line up**. Poke a paper fastener through both circles and secure. This is your **code wheel**!

3

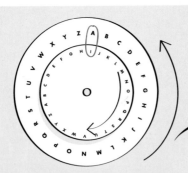

To code a message, turn the **smaller** wheel so that the two alphabets don't match up. Find **A** on the big wheel and make a note of **the letter** below it.

4

Write that letter at the top of your message (this will set your 'shift key'). **Keeping the two circles in position**, code your message by **replacing** each 'proper' letter from the small circle with the letter above it on the top circle.

5

Give the letter and the wheel to your friend. They must line the wheel up so that **A** on the big wheel is above **the letter** you wrote at the top of your message (the shift key), then use the wheel to **decipher your code**.

TOP
TIP
Different positions of the wheels change the code! **Always write down the shift key letter!**

INCOMING
AIR
Mail

Follow the steps to make special **paper aeroplanes** that can carry **hidden messages**. Just don't let them fly into Miss Trunchbull's hands or she'll throw them (and probably you) clear out of the window!

DIFFICULTY RATING:

YOU WILL NEED:
- A PIECE OF A4 PAPER
- A PAPER STRAW
- SCISSORS
- STICKY TAPE
- A SMALL PIECE OF PAPER WITH YOUR MESSAGE ON

What to do:

Matilda's PHENOMENAL **FACT**

The wings of your paper plane are **thicker at the front**, which helps the plane to fly.

1

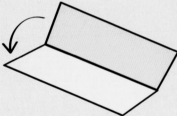

Fold the piece of A4 paper in **half lengthwise**, as shown.

2

Open out the paper and fold in the **top corners to the crease in the middle** to make a triangle shape.

3

Fold the triangle shape down so that **the tip meets the middle crease**.

72

4 Fold down the corners at the top so that they meet **just above the tip of the triangle**, as shown.

5 **Fold up the tip** of the triangle so that it **overlaps the folded-down parts** and holds them in place.

6 **Turn the paper over**, then fold it in half down the middle crease and smooth down the creases.

7 Make the wings by **folding down both sides**, as shown.

8 Cut the **paper straw to the length of your aeroplane** and tape it to the bottom.

9 **Roll up** your secret message and slip it inside the straw.

10 **Throw your plane** to send the secret hidden message!

TOP **TIP**
You can **turn the corners** of your aeroplane's **wings up or down** slightly to help it **steer**.

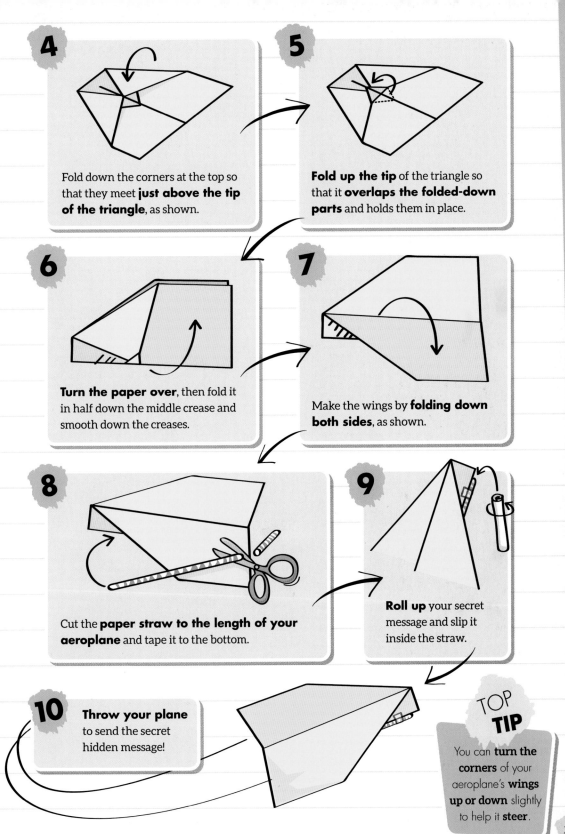

RIDICULOUSLY GOOD *Riddles*

Matilda is a **whizz with words**, and confuses adults (even those who think they are clever) with her extraordinary vocabulary. Amaze your audience with these **brilliant riddles**, then follow the tips to make up your own.

TOP **TIP**

Practise saying these riddles and teasers **out loud**, so you know them off by heart!

What has a **FACE** and TWO HANDS, but no arms or legs?
A CLOCK!

Pneumonoultramicroscopicsilicovolcanoconiosis is the LONGEST WORD in the DICTIONARY. Spell it.
I-T (it).

What begins with 'T', ends with 'T' and has 'T' in it?
A TEAPOT.

If I have it, I do not share it; if I share it, I do not have it. What is it?
A SECRET.

Name THREE DAYS that are **next to each other** without saying Monday, Wednesday or Friday.
YESTERDAY, **TODAY** and TOMORROW!

DARING DEED

Try making up funny riddles about your family or **teachers**! Think about their **funny traits** and include them in a riddle to see if people can guess who you are talking about. If they're a little rude, you can always write them using your code wheel!

I have LOTS OF KEYS, but I CAN'T open anything. What am I?

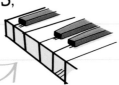

A PIANO.

The more you take away, the LARGER it becomes. What is it?
A HOLE.

I'm super light, but even the STRONGEST PERSON in the world can't hold me for longer than **10 MINUTES**. What am I?

BREATH!

1 Think of a **good subject**. It's important to choose something that's **familiar** to lots of people, but let your marvellous brain go wild.

2 Write down a **list** of different things that **describe your subject**. What does it look like? What **colour** and **shape** is it? Does it **smell**, **taste** or **sound** like anything? (Maybe it's terribly disgusting!) What do you use it for? All these words might be useful for writing your riddle.

3 Think about **what type of riddle** you would like to write. It could be a **'What am I?'** riddle, or a **simple question**, or even a **rhyme**. For example:

She's a **mighty** headmistress
And a MEAN MACHINE.
If you're not very careful,
She'll toss you in a **ravine**!

(Answer: **Miss Trunchbull**)

4 You can also have the **answer** as part of the rhyme, like this:

Her name is SWEET
And so too is **SHE**.
Matilda and friends
Call her _ _ _ _ _ _ _ _ _.

(Answer: **Miss Honey**)

5 Once you've written your riddle, PRACTISE, **PRACTISE**, **PRACTISE** until you know it off by heart.

GROWN-UP BRAIN BAMBOOZLING!

Make **gormless grown-ups** think they are losing their minds – just like Matilda does to her parents and the Trunchbull – by doing this **simple trick**.

DIFFICULTY RATING: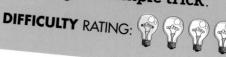

What to do:

1 Write down lots of **colour names** in a **different colour from the colour name** you are writing. Confused? Here is an example:

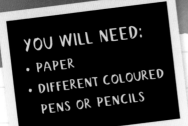

RED GREEN YELLOW BLUE

BLUE PINK GREEN RED

ORANGE PURPLE BLUE PINK

BLACK GREEN RED BROWN

GREEN YELLOW BROWN ORANGE

2 Show a **grown-up** your list and challenge them to **name the colours the words are written in** (rather than reading out the words themselves) as quickly as they can. They'll soon be getting their words (and their brains) in a tangle!

Matilda's PHENOMENAL **FACT**

This famous effect is named after **J. Ridley Stroop**, who discovered it in the 1930s. It works because the **words interfere with your ability to name the colour**. There are two theories that may explain it:

The Speed of Processing Theory: this says that the interference occurs because words are read faster than colours are named.

The Selective Attention Theory: this says that the interference occurs because naming colours requires more attention than reading words.

DARING **DEED**

ADULT REVENGE BONUS!

This trick may actually have better results with adults than with younger children, as they are more used to reading! You could try **timing each person** and comparing reaction times.

Face
FLASHCARDS

Not everyone's **memory** is as astounding as Matilda's. **Train your brain** to remember faces you don't know using these fun **flashcards**.

 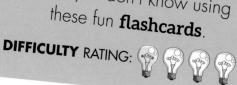

YOU WILL NEED:
- MAGAZINES SHOWING PICTURES OF PEOPLE IN THEM
- SCISSORS
- PIECES OF CARD THAT ARE THE SAME SIZE
- A PEN

What to do:

1

Cut out a selection of **faces of people you don't know** from magazines and stick each one on to a piece of card.

2

BRUCE BOGTROTTER

Write the name of the person on the **back** of each card.

3

Mix up the cards and then **just look at the faces**. How many names can you remember?

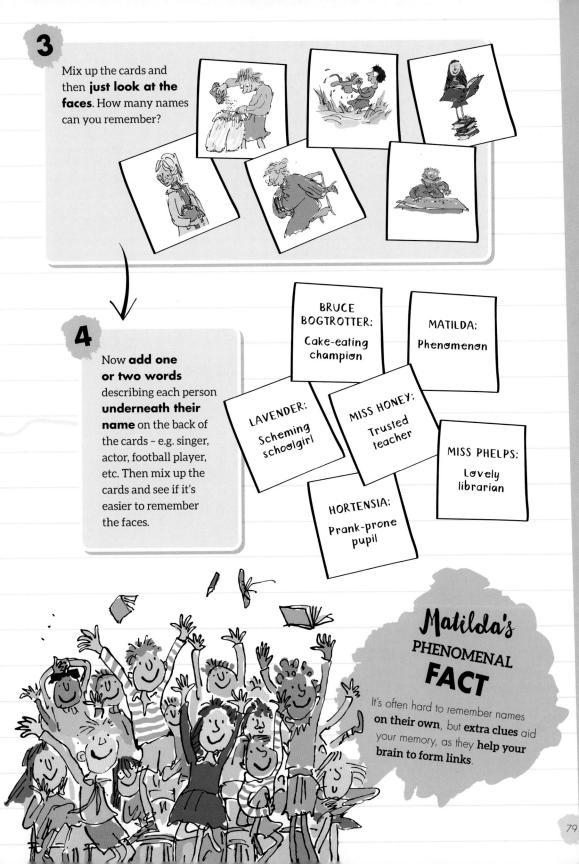

4

Now **add one or two words** describing each person **underneath their name** on the back of the cards – e.g. singer, actor, football player, etc. Then mix up the cards and see if it's easier to remember the faces.

BRUCE BOGTROTTER:
Cake-eating champion

MATILDA:
Phenomenon

LAVENDER:
Scheming schoolgirl

MISS HONEY:
Trusted teacher

MISS PHELPS:
Lovely librarian

HORTENSIA:
Prank-prone pupil

Matilda's PHENOMENAL FACT

It's often hard to remember names **on their own**, but **extra clues** aid your memory, as they **help your brain to form links**.

Lovely LIMERICKS

Matilda made up this very good **limerick** about her teacher, Miss Honey. Read it, and then use the **rules and tips** to help you make up your own.

DIFFICULTY RATING: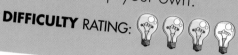

LIMERICK Rules

Limericks are **five lines** long.

The **first line usually ends** with someone's **name** or a **place name**.

LINE **1**	The thing we all ask about **JENNY**
LINE **2**	Is, 'Surely there cannot be **MANY**
LINE **3**	Young girls in the PLACE
LINE **4**	With so lovely a FACE?'
LINE **5**	The answer to that is, 'Not **ANY**!'

The **last words** of lines **1**, **2** and **5** must rhyme.

The **last words** of lines **3** and **4** must rhyme.

The **rhythm** is very distinctive. The **first two lines** and the **last line** have **three stressed beats** in them (da DUM, da da DUM, da da DUM da).

The **THING**	we all **ASK**	about **JENNY**
da DUM	da da DUM	da da DUM da

The **third and fourth lines** have **two beats** in them (da DUM, da da DUM). The 'DUM' words are usually emphasized.

Young **GIRLS**	in the **PLACE**
da DUM	da da DUM

The rhythm doesn't need to be exactly as above, but it should sound close to it when you read your limerick. The 'DUM' part of the rhythm is **emphasized** or **stressed** when you say the word.

TOP **TIPS**

1 Choose a name of a **person** or **place** and write the first line.

2 Use a **rhyming dictionary** to find words that rhyme with the name.

RHYMING DICTIONARY

3 Write lines **2** and **5** to **rhyme** with the **first line**, and then lines **3** and **4** to rhyme with **each other**. Try to make **line 5 funny**.

My GENIUS NOTES

Use these two pages to write about all the **rebellious** and **mischievous tricks**, **illusions** and **experiments** you have done and what happened!

HOW MANY HAVE YOU READ?

     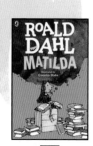

☐ ☐ ☐ ☐ ☐ ☐

☐ ☐ ☐ ☐ ☐ ☐

☐ ☐ ☐ ☐ ☐

FEWER THAN 5? WHOOPSY-SPLUNKERS! You've got some reading to do!

BETWEEN 5 AND 10? Wonderful surprises await! Keep reading . . .

MORE THAN 10? Whoopee! Which was your favourite?